FLIG
UNITE STATES
OF AMERICA

Story by
DAVID SCOTT DANIELL

Illustrated by
JACK MATTHEW

Publishers : Wills & Hepworth Ltd., Loughborough

First Published 1959   ©   *Printed in England*

FLIGHT THREE :
UNITED STATES OF AMERICA

Alison opened her eyes and wondered where she was. Then, as she yawned, she remembered. She was flying to America. Through the window of the air-liner she saw a sea of pink cotton-wool far below. It was the top of the clouds, tinged pink by the rising sun. Thousands of feet below the clouds was the Atlantic Ocean.

Everyone else in the air-liner seemed to be asleep, with their seats tilted back to make beds. At her side, her brother John was sleeping soundly with his nose tucked into his rug. Daddy seemed to be asleep, too, but when she looked at him he opened his eyes, winked at her and shut them again. You never knew with Daddy.

The stewardess came down the passage-way between the seats, very neat and efficient, and took a tray of coffee through the forward door. Alison had a glimpse of an officer at the controls, and of another bending over a chart on a table. While the passengers slept peacefully, these clever men were flying their beautiful air-liner at several hundred miles an hour high above the ocean, from London to New York. Alison snuggled down into her rug and, like John, tucked her nose inside. Yesterday they had said good-bye to Mummy and little Peter and Mary at London Airport. Soon they would be in America. Alison fell asleep.

. . . . . .

Everyone was now wide awake. They had had breakfast, an exciting meal on trays with partitions, and soon they would be landing. Alison and John looked out of the window at New York City below them—the gateway to the United States of America.

Daddy had come to America on business and Alison and John had a week to spend in New York. They had a fine time exploring the busy, bustling streets; some of them like canyons with immensely tall buildings on either side, others wide and spacious. They went to parks and museums and ate wonderful ice-creams in " drug-stores," which were much more than chemist shops. One of their joys was riding swiftly upwards in the fast lifts—which they soon learned to call elevators—to their rooms on the twenty-eighth floor of the hotel.

But the most exciting lift ride was when Daddy took them to the top of the Empire State Building, the tallest sky-scraper in the world. It is a hundred-and-two stories high, and they had a wonderful view from the observation floor near the top.

" Why do they have these sky-scrapers, Daddy? " John asked.

" For a very good reason," said Daddy. " The early settlers, three-hundred years ago, built their new city on an island, because it was easier to defend it from the Indians."

" I see," said Alison, " and the town grew and grew, and because it was on an island they had to build upwards! "

" That's it. Land is very valuable in New York. Fortunately it is thick rock so it is quite safe to build these very tall buildings. This is the tallest of them all, and with the television mast on the top it is over fourteen-hundred feet high, four times as high as St. Paul's Cathedral in London."

Alison was gazing down at the network of crowded streets. " So once this island was all wild country," she said, "and the brave settlers in the New World risked death from the Indians. Now look at it! "

" The busiest and the richest city in the world," said Daddy.

One evening Daddy let Alison and John stay up late so that they could see New York after dark. They had a fine supper in a restaurant and afterwards they strolled down Broadway, the long street where all the theatres are. It was a blaze of coloured lights of all kinds, and full of motor cars and people. They went into a drug-store where Daddy had a cup of coffee and the children had milk drinks.

" Well, what do you know about America? " Daddy asked them.

" You have a lot to eat," said John promptly. " Enormous breakfasts, starting with fruit-juice, and lots of meat for dinner."

" I didn't mean food," Daddy said.

" I think I've got the money worked out," said Alison. " A dollar is about seven shillings, and five cents is about fourpence."

John opened his notebook, where he collected facts. " The population of New York City is 7,981,957," he read, " and it is the biggest city in the United States of America."

" You know," said Alison thoughtfully, " it's nice of them to speak English. They could have their own language! "

" That's because English people settled here first," Daddy explained. " America was a British colony until 1776."

" The names of towns show that," said John. " I was looking at a map. Round about here there's Manchester, Plymouth, Bradford, Cambridge—oh, ever so many."

" And the name of New York itself," said Alison.

8

When they had spent a week in New York, Daddy hired a car to go to Washington, which was two-hundred miles to the south-west. They drove along a wonderful modern highway, where everyone went very fast—and on the right-hand side of the road, too. They went through many towns and two great cities, Philadelphia and Baltimore.

When they had been to their hotel they set out to explore the capital of the United States. Washington proved to be a splendid city of very wide avenues and streets on the banks of the River Potomac. There were lovely parks and gardens, most striking of all, a great number of magnificent buildings and monuments.

They went to have a look at the Capitol first, a great domed building with a pillared front. Alison took out her sketch book to make a drawing, and John pulled his notebook from his pocket and licked the point of his pencil.

" Want something for your book, John ? " Daddy asked. " Well, put down that Washington is called after the first President of the United States, General George Washington. He decided to have the capital of the country here, and supervised its design."

" Does the President live here ? " Alison asked.

" Yes, in the White House. We'll go there next. This is the Capitol, where the Senate and the House of Representatives meet to govern the country."

Suddenly they heard the roar of engines. Two large motor cars were coming down the road, led by policemen riding high powered motor cycles. In the first car was a very distinguished foreign visitor, going to see the President in the White House.

A short drive of fifteen miles from Washington took them to Mount Vernon, the home of George Washington. They went over the lovely, old wooden mansion, overlooking the River Potomac, and then sat under a tree in the garden.

" George Washington's great-grandfather came from England," Daddy told them. " His father was a prosperous tobacco planter. This State of Virginia is famous for growing tobacco. When the colonies rebelled against Britain, George Washington became a soldier, and eventually he commanded the American Army. When America won her independence, Washington was made the President of the new country. I suppose it was George Washington more than anyone else who brought the United States of America into being."

" How big was America in those days? " Alison asked.

" Get out the map, John," said Daddy; and when the map was unfolded and spread on the grass they all looked at it.

" In 1789, when Washington became President, America was only this north-east corner, up here; thirteen states only. That is where the settlers had come. All the rest was unexplored, full of wild animals and Indians."

" It is a *big* country! " said John.

" It's very big. See New York State, up in the corner? That is nearly as big as England. The United States of America stretch from Canada in the north right down to Mexico in the south; and from the Atlantic coast in the east to the Pacific coast in the west is three thousand miles. There are a hundred-and-seventy million Americans. You see the map is divided up into forty-eight states, and there's a forty-ninth, Alaska, away to the north-west of Canada."

Alison looked at the old white mansion. " And the man who started it all lived in that house! " she said.

Their next journey was by train, five-hundred miles westwards from Washington to Frankfort, the capital of the State of Kentucky. It was an exciting journey through the Allegheny Mountains into a rich and rolling country-side beyond. It was so late when they arrived, they went to bed at once at the air-conditioned, very modern hotel.

After breakfast next morning, Daddy opened the map and showed them where they were. " Here is Frankfort," he said, " and here is the State of Kentucky, between Illinois, Indiana and Ohio to the north, and Tennessee to the south. They call Kentucky the ' Blue Grass State '."

" Blue grass!" said Alison. " Grass is green."

" You'll see what they mean this afternoon. We'll hire a car and go for a drive in the country."

In the afternoon they went for a drive through the glorious rolling countryside, with smart white fences everywhere. They stopped by a river to admire the view.

" Look," said John, " I see why they call it blue grass. It's green really, but it has a kind of blue bloom!"

" It's very special grass," Daddy explained. " They send the seed all over the world. And look there!"

Two beautiful young horses were playing in a huge field beside the road. They galloped by at a great pace, tossing their heads as they flashed past.

" Oh, aren't they *beautiful*!" Alison exclaimed.

" Kentucky is world-famous for breeding race-horses," said Daddy. " There are a great number of breeding establishments, and Kentucky horses are among the fastest in the world. The Kentucky Derby is a great national event. Those were young race-horses."

" What a place!" said John. " Blue grass, white fences and race-horses!"

" I'd like to live in Kentucky," Alison said.

Three peaceful days in Kentucky ended with another train journey, five-hundred miles north through Illinois, to the great city of Chicago on the shores of Lake Michigan. Daddy had a lot of business to do, but Alison and John were very well looked after by Brent, the son of one of his business friends.

Brent was a cheerful boy of great energy, and he threw himself heart and soul into the task of taking his young English friends round his beloved Chicago. They explored the busy streets, teeming with traffic, and the beautiful boulevards alongside Lake Michigan, which is so big that it looks like the sea. Brent showed them the great sky-scrapers and the monuments, the big stores and the museums.

One afternoon he took them to Lincoln Park to see the famous Zoo, and afterwards they had a swim.

" Well, what do you think of Chicago?" Brent asked them as they lay sunbathing.

" Oh, it's hard to say," said Alison, " it's so *big*!"

" It sure is," said Brent proudly. " Everything's big here. Chicago's the second largest city in the States. Four million people live in Chicago, and seventeen million visitors come here every year from all over the world!"

" Like Alison and me," said John.

" They call Chicago the ' bread-basket of the nation'," Brent went on, " because we handle the food grown on the farms in the Middle West. We've got the biggest railway system in the world and more different industries than anywhere else; meat canning, machinery, coal and oil, and nearly everything. Let's get dressed and I'll take you to see the docks."

An hour later they were at the docks, watching steel being loaded into big ships.

The next day Brent took Alison and John to the railway yards as part of their tour of Chicago. This was a special treat for John, who loved trains. They stood on a bridge and looked down on the complicated maze of railway lines and watched a score of engines busily shunting trains of long wagons, while others stood at the dozens of loading bays. An important looking passenger train thundered past under the bridge, bound for the Pacific coast, two thousand miles away.

" What do you think of all this? " Brent asked proudly.

" It's *wonderful!* " John said, his eyes shining.

" It's certainly a very big place," Alison said politely.

" The Chicago railway yards are the largest in the world," said Brent. Then he blushed and looked embarrassed. " I guess you think I'm always saying that!"

" Always saying what? " Alison asked him.

" Why, how big everything is here in Chicago, and how it's the best in the world. My Pop says you Britishers are touchy about boasting."

" But we don't mind a bit," said Alison, " truly we don't. And everything here *is* big—the sky-scrapers, the motor cars, the meals, the country—and this huge railway yard!"

" You're sure you don't mind?" Brent asked, looking relieved. He told them more about Chicago.

" You see, everything here is so new compared with England. Why, in 1830 there were only fifty people living here, now there are four millions. It was only a fort, called Fort Dearborn, the furthest outpost of the

States. In England it's all old and quaint and picturesque, so we have to make up for it in size."

" We think Chicago's wonderful, Brent," said Alison.

" And I've never seen such a lot of trains," John said.

On their last day in Chicago, Brent's father took them all to a baseball game. The enormous stadium was packed with excited people. Daddy explained that baseball was like English rounders, only much faster, rougher, and more grown-up. He said that baseball was as important to Americans as Test cricket was to Englishmen.

Brent explained the rules to Alison and John, but they couldn't really understand the very complicated scoring. Alison and John enjoyed the match, and saw that it was certainly a very hard, tough game.

After the match Brent's father took them all out to supper, and John tried to explain cricket to Brent. But he had to give up; cricket is not an easy game to explain to an American boy who has never seen it.

The next day they went to the airport to fly five-hundred miles west to Nebraska, to visit some cousins who had a farm. They flew over the States of Illinois and Iowa to Lincoln in Nebraska, they then went by train for a hundred miles to a small station where their Uncle Joe met them.

Finally, they went in his large, modern car forty miles through an endless vista of golden wheat to the farm. There was a warm welcome from Auntie Elise and their cousins Bill and Dolly and, as always in America, a large and delicious supper.

Alison and John spent ten very happy days with their American cousins, a welcome rest after all their travelling and sight-seeing. Uncle Joe's farm was a splendid place for a holiday; there was so much modern machinery that John said it looked more like a factory than a farm. They spent every day in the open air and went back in the evening to the comfortable farmhouse with enormous appetites, which Auntie Elise was delighted to satisfy.

It was beautiful country and the great spaces and quietness felt strange after the bustle and crowds of New York and Chicago. One day they were having a picnic with hamburgers—very large and delicious beef patties—when Alison said: " It doesn't seem possible that there could be so much wheat!"

She and John gazed at the wheat, golden in the sunshine, which stretched to the horizon in every direction.

" The Middle West, that's this part of the States, is called the larder of the world for bread and meat," said Dolly.

"We produce the wheat for bread in this part," Bill added, " and they produce all the beef in the other parts. The whole of the middle of the country is one rich farm."

" Daddy said that America's so rich because she produces all her own food," said John.

" That's right," said Bill. " In the Middle West here we feed all the hundred-and-seventy million people in the States, and we send food to countries all over the world as well."

" Everything is produced in America," said Dolly, " except coffee and tea."

" It's all so *big*," said Alison, biting her hamburger, " and so *rich*!"

" Yes, it sure is something, being an American," said Bill.

They were lucky enough to be staying with Uncle Joe on July 4th, which is a great day in America. It is Independence Day and a national holiday, and nearly everyone has a picnic and fireworks. When they were sitting in the porch before the picnic, John asked what Independence Day was.

" It's the anniversary of the Declaration of Independence," Uncle Joe explained, " when the British colonists in America declared solemnly that they wanted to be an independent nation, and broke away from Great Britain. It was in 1776, on the 4th of July."

" We learnt the Declaration of Independence at school," said Bill, and he recited a passage from it. " 'We hold these truths to be self-evident, that all men are created equal; that they are endowed by their Creator with certain inalienable rights; and among these are life, liberty and the pursuit of happiness'."

" Come into the house," said Dolly. " We've got a picture of the signing of the Declaration of Independence."

In the living room Dolly got out the picture and Uncle Joe explained how brave it was of the colonists to defy the might of Britain. He told them about the war which lasted six years, until, in 1782, Great Britain recognised America as a separate and independent nation.

" The signing of that document," he said, " was the birth of the United States of America."

Auntie Elise then came in and said, " Let's go into the backyard for our picnic. Everything's ready, Joe, you can barbecue the steaks."

As they all trooped out John said: " My word! A real barbecue, and fireworks afterwards!"

24

Alison was sitting on a rock with her sketch book on her knees. Daddy was lying on his back enjoying an after-lunch nap, and John was sitting watching a tin of treacle which Daddy had put on a rock twenty yards away. Birds were singing in the trees and a stream in the gorge was making its own music as it danced between the stones. They might have been the last humans left in the world.

They were in Yellowstone National Park in Wyoming. They had left the farm three days before and had travelled another five-hundred miles westwards to the Rocky Mountains. This time they had come in a luxury motor coach, and they had slept in a hotel built like a very large log cabin. They were enjoying a quiet day in the wild grandeur of one of the most beautiful parts of America.

Suddenly John went tense, shook Daddy to wake him up, and whispered—" Look, they've come!"

They all watched, sitting quite still. A black bear had come from among the trees, followed by two tubby baby bears. She looked round, gazed for a moment at the three humans, and then calmly lumbered over to the treacle tin, followed by her cubs. She picked up the tin, sniffed it, grunted with pleasure, and sat down, while the cubs stood expectantly beside her. Then the mother bear held the tin against her thigh with one paw and dipped the other into the treacle—and licked it. After she had taken a dozen licks she held it out and the babies did the same.

Daddy got his camera and took some photographs. Alison and John sat entranced, while the three bears feasted.

They had a wonderful time in Yellowstone National Park, where they saw more black bears and other wild animals. John kept a list of the animals they saw, and he thought he had seen an enormous grizzly bear in the distance. When he was making notes he asked how large Yellowstone Park was.

" It covers more than three thousand square miles," Daddy said, " and that's—well—about the same size as two English counties."

" Two whole counties for a park!" said Alison. " How lovely for the wild animals!"

" And nice for the people too," said Daddy. " The Government has set aside a number of particularly beautiful districts as National Parks so that they will never be spoiled. All the wild animals and birds are absolutely safe and people can see them in their natural homes. They have elk and deer, moose, bison and antelopes, bears—black and grizzly—and even wolves."

The next day they went to see *Old Faithful* the famous geyser, or hot spring. Alison asked why it was called *Old Faithful*. " Because it's so reliable," Daddy explained. " There are more than a hundred geysers in Yellowstone Park, but this one is unique because it erupts about every sixty-three minutes, so they call it *Old Faithful*. You'll see."

They waited with the other people in a large circle round the geyser. People looked at their watches and then, suddenly, a great column of scalding water shot a hundred-and-fifty feet into the air with a hissing roar and a cloud of steam. The wonderful sight lasted for five minutes and then stopped. *Old Faithful* would be quiet for another hour.

They spent three days in Yellowstone National Park and then they continued their journey in the motor-coach through the magnificent scenery of the Rocky Mountains. Once when they had stopped for lunch Alison made a sketch of the road and the mountains while John gazed down on a great express thundering along the railway below the road.

" What a wonderful road this is!" Alison said.

" The Americans are first-class engineers," Daddy said. " Their country was opened up by the roads and railways. Let's have a look at the map, John, and I'll show you what I mean."

John opened the map. " Look," said Daddy, " there are two important mountain chains in America, the Appalachians down the east side, and here in the west the mighty Rockies, which start in Canada up in the north. At first the colonists stayed on the eastern fringe, then they crossed the Appalachians and gradually opened up the middle of the country, pushing their trails westwards and making towns and farms. And, of course, all the while, there were the Indians to deal with."

" Ah, the Indians!" John said eagerly.

" I'll tell you about them in a minute. The Rocky Mountains were a problem to the settlers pushing westwards, but gradually brave pioneers made trails across them and got through to the Pacific coast. First they used the rough trails, then proper roads were made, and then the railways were built and fine modern roads. The great roads and the railways stretch right across America now, from the Atlantic to the Pacific. These roads and railways have made America."

" Tell us about the pioneers, Daddy," John said.

" So you want to know about the pioneer days," said Daddy.

" Yes please," Alison said. " Was this a pioneer trail?"

" Most likely it was. Everything would have been just as it is now except that the road would have been no more than a track; there would be no railway, and that fine bridge would only be a rough and ready wooden one."

Alison and John looked round them imagining the scene as it was a hundred years ago.

" The Pioneers would come along this trail," Daddy went on, " seeking new land in the west. All their possessions would be in the covered wagons. The older men would drive the wagons and the younger ones would ride alongside on horseback, with their rifles handy."

" Because of the Indians?" asked John eagerly.

" Yes, to protect themselves from the Indians and to shoot game for food. It was a very dangerous journey; they might overturn a wagon on the rough track, or get stranded miles from anywhere, and always there were the hostile Indians."

" Why were the Indians hostile?" asked Alison.

" It was their country and they knew very well that when the Palefaces came many more would follow them and settle. Their hunting grounds would be turned into farmland, and villages and towns would be built. The Palefaces shot the buffaloes, too, and that was the main food of the Redskins."

" I can imagine the covered wagons coming down this very road," said Alison, "a hundred years ago!"

" And I can imagine the Redskins shooting at them from behind those rocks," said John, "and from this side too!"

They took to the air again after their motor-coach drive through the Rocky Mountains, and flew south-west over Idaho and Nevada to California, to visit San Francisco. As they came in they had a wonderful view of the great city around its famous harbour, with the Golden Gate Bridge proudly spanning the entrance.

Daddy told them that San Francisco was the biggest port on the Pacific Coast of America, and that it was one of the largest and safest land-locked harbours in the world. He said that the Golden Gate was more than a mile wide. John wrote these facts down in his notebook.

There was much to see in San Francisco; quaint old buildings as well as beautiful modern ones. They had a ride on the famous cable-car and saw some of the forty-six parks in the city. It was gloriously warm and they passed many happy hours swimming in the sea and sun-bathing on the golden sands.

" Well, you two," Daddy said, " this is California, called the 'playground of America', because of its lovely climate!"

" I like San Francisco," said John. " It's different somehow—more foreign than the other places we've seen."

" California was Spanish once," Daddy said, " part of Mexico, which lies to the south. California became part of the United States in 1848. In those days San Francisco was quite cut off from the rest of the country by the Rocky Mountains. Then they got a mail service through, called the Pony Express, and in 1869 the railway was finished, and San Francisco was joined to the rest of the United States. But the name San Francisco is Spanish."

Daddy hired a car one day and took Alison and John for a long drive out of San Francisco. When they had left the city behind them they noticed that the road was lined for many miles with orange groves, loaded with delicious looking fruit.

"Here's something for your notebook John, my boy," said Daddy. "California produces an enormous quantity of oranges, grapefruit, and all citrous fruits."

"It's the lovely climate, I suppose," said Alison.

"Ten-out-of-ten!" Daddy said. "And something else—gold. They discovered gold in California a hundred years ago, and people poured in from all over America and from all over the world, hoping to get a fortune quickly. They were pretty rough types who came, and for ten years it was all very ugly and lawless. But in time order was restored. Anyhow, California has gold, and golden fruit, and golden sunshine."

"And the Golden Gate of San Francisco," said John.

The road climbed up into mountainous country. After a while Alison said suddenly, "Daddy, look at those trees! Just *look* at them!"

"Gracious!" said John, "they're *enormous*!"

"That's what I've brought you to see," said Daddy. "They're the American redwood. People say that America is a new country, but it's got the oldest living things in the world, these redwood trees. Some of them are from two to three thousand years old, and more than three-hundred feet tall, nearly as high as St. Paul's Cathedral."

"Look at that one," said John, pointing ahead. "There's a tunnel cut into it and the road goes through it."

"And we're going to drive through it. Here we go!"

"My goodness!" said Alison, "driving *through* a tree!"

When Daddy had finished his business in San Francisco they went south by train to Los Angeles, three-hundred-and-fifty miles down the coast. They spent a few days there, and Alison was thrilled to see some of the homes of American film stars, and they had a glimpse of Hollywood, where films are made.

From Los Angeles they flew east for three-hundred-and-fifty miles to the city of Phoenix, the capital of Arizona. One day they went by car to an Indian village and bought presents; a blanket for Mummy, a tomahawk for young Peter, and a doll for Mary. They were all made by the Indians. Daddy explained that the Indians were the original inhabitants of America, and the Government had set aside certain areas all over the country where those Indians who wished could live in their traditional manner.

For a special treat, Daddy arranged to take them two-hundred miles north to see the famous Grand Canyon. They went by aeroplane to the Grand Canyon National Park. Most of the country was bare and wild, and in parts it was desert, with nothing but strangely shaped cacti growing.

They spent a long time wandering about the wild and rugged wonderland of rocks. The Grand Canyon is a mighty chasm, in places a mile deep, and nearly three-hundred miles long. It has been worn out of the rocks over hundreds of thousands of years by the Colorado River. The strange shapes, the red colouring of the rocks, and the many shades of green, brown and pink within the canyon were quite marvellous.

The next journey was a thousand miles by train from Phoenix in Arizona, across New Mexico, to Houston in Texas. Daddy explained that although they were only crossing three States the journey was longer than from the north of Scotland to the south of England. Texas itself is twice as big as England and Wales.

They spent two days at El Paso on the frontier between the United States and Mexico, and they had the thrill of going into the neighbouring town of Cuidad Juarez in Mexico. Everyone spoke Spanish and the Mexican flag was flying.

From El Paso they went on into Texas, the train running for hour after hour over endless plains. Alison asked Daddy why they called Texas the 'Lone Star State.'

" For a short time Texas was a country on its own," Daddy said. "It was won from Mexico in 1836, and it had its own President and its own flag, with one star. But the hostile Indians and the marauding Mexicans were more than Texas could deal with alone, so in 1845 it became part of the United States." John wrote that down in his notebook.

Later on, when they were drinking iced lemonade, John suddenly pointed out of the carriage window. " Look!" he said excitedly. " Look, there's a cowboy, a real genuine cowboy, on a horse!"

Sitting on a fine horse on a little hill was a bronzed and handsome man in a wide brimmed hat. He wore a check shirt and had a lasso coiled at the front of his saddle.

" Is he a real cowboy?" John asked, gazing out of the window as the train sped across Texas.

" Yes, but nowadays they are called cow-hands," said Daddy. " There are two more in the distance, see them? They are looking after that herd of cattle. Texas is in the Great Plains of America, and there are splendid pastures for raising cattle. Most of the cattle have gone to the north now. You see, as the season goes on, the cow-hands drive the cattle northwards, to be able to eat the fresher grass."

" Daddy," Alison asked, " what are the Texas Rangers exactly?"

" Ah! They belong to the old days, when Texas was very wild. Lawless men used to steal cattle and land. They worked in gangs, and they used to shoot quickly. The Government formed the Texas Rangers to suppress the cattle thieves, and keep law and order."

" They were jolly good shots, too," said John, and as the train thundered across the width of Texas they talked about cowboys and sheriffs, ranches and rustlers.

" Now look out of the other window," Daddy said after a while. " You've seen the cowboys from the old days. Over there is something that belongs to modern America."

" Whatever is it?" asked Alison.

" I know," said John. " It's oil!"

" Oil it is!" Daddy agreed. " That's a petrol re-fining plant. The south of America is very rich in oil. They find it in deep wells, and it's brought by pipes to plants like that, where it's refined into petrol. The great silvered spheres are for storing it."

They spent four days in Houston, in yet another very modern hotel with a wonderful elevator, as they now called the lift. They did some sight-seeing, and swam in the warm sea of the Gulf of Mexico. The next journey was three-hundred miles by train to the colourful city of New Orleans, the great seaport of the State of Louisiana.

A business friend of Daddy's, Mr. Carlyon, had invited them to stay with him. They went fifty miles up the great Mississippi River in a steamboat, and then by car to Mr. Carlyon's home. It was a beautiful, old white house, with a pillared front, in a perfectly kept garden which went down to the river. It was as lovely inside as out, with large cool rooms, fine furniture and handsome pictures. Everything about the house, and about the Carlyon family, too, was gracious.

Mr. Carlyon's son, Desmond, was about Alison's age. He was a slender, good looking boy, kind and courteous, and he spoke with a soft, southern accent. When the grown-ups were chatting over their coffee after dinner, Desmond took Alison and John into the garden and down to the river.

The moon was shining, and in the moonlight the Mississippi looked magic, and the old house looked lovelier than ever.

" Listen!" said Alison suddenly. " How lovely!"

Nearby a negro started to play the guitar softly, and he sang some southern song with a haunting melody. The night was warm, the air was soft, and everything was beautiful.

" Yes," said Desmond quietly, " this is the spirit of the Deep South, my home!"

The next day Desmond showed them a portrait in his father's study. It was a painting of a gentleman in uniform. " That's my great-grandfather," said Desmond proudly.

John read the printing underneath the picture. " Colonel Desmond Carlyon. Killed at Gettysburg, 1863."

" That was in the American Civil War, wasn't it?" Alison asked. " What started it?"

" It was over the question of negro slaves," Desmond explained. " We used slaves from Africa in the south to work in our cotton and tobacco plantations. The Government in the north told us to set them free. We refused to be ordered about by the north and so went to war. Twenty-three northern states against eleven in the south. It was a terrible war, with thousands killed. It lasted four years, but in the end the north won. My grandfather was killed at the Battle of Gettysburg."

" He was fighting for the south, I suppose," said John.

" Of course," said Desmond. " They said he was a fine soldier."

" I'm sure he was," said Alison. " And when it was over, north and south became friends, did they?"

" We were united again," said Desmond, " but it took fifty years to get over it. All ended well, however, and we became one country, under Old Glory."

" Old Glory?" said John. " What's that?"

" Our flag, the Stars and Stripes," Desmond said. " Let's get my canoe out and go on the river."

They had a wonderful trip up the Mississippi in Desmond's canoe.

" The Indians call the Mississippi 'The Father of Waters'," said Desmond. " It's the greatest river in America."

Mr. Carlyon and Desmond took their English friends in their car to see the cotton fields. They watched the negroes moving slowly across the sun-drenched fields, picking the fluffy white balls of cotton and putting them in sacks. Mr. Carlyon and Daddy started talking about cotton costs of production and export prices, so the three children wandered off. They sat on a fence to watch a cheerful old man who was singing to himself as he expertly picked the cotton.

" We saw a lot of negroes in the north," said Alison, " but there seems to be many more in the south."

" They're all full American citizens," said Desmond. " They are the descendants of the slaves who were brought from Africa in the bad old days, but they are as American now as the descendants of the people who came over in the Mayflower."

" It's wonderful to think," said Alison, " that when that little ship sailed from England three-hundred years ago it was the birth of this great nation!"

" That was the start," Desmond said. " The English founded the new colonies on the east coast—they called it the 'New World.' After we broke away from Britain people came from every land, people who wanted to make a new start in the 'Land of the Free'. British, Germans, Poles, Russians, Italians, every European race; and Chinese and Japanese came to the Western states. But they are all Americans."

" And they all speak English!" John said.

" America and Britain are like cousins, really," said Desmond. "We have the same ideas of freedom and justice. We're good friends and when there's trouble— why, we stand together!"

On the last evening with their friends they had a barbecue—a wonderful picnic supper cooked in the open air. They ate all manner of good things and sang old songs under the great southern moon.

When they said good-bye to the Carlyon family they went to New Orleans to fly back to New York. The flight was twelve-hundred miles north-east over the states of Mississippi, Alabama, North Carolina, Virginia, Maryland, and New Jersey. Daddy had to spend two days in New York, and then they went on board the air-liner for England.

" Well," said Daddy, when they had taken-off and had unfastened their safety-belts, " what do you two travellers think of the United States of America?"

" It's very *big*," said John, " and very friendly."

" It's so varied," Alison said. " We've seen great teeming cities with sky-scrapers, like New York, Chicago and San Francisco, and huge empty areas, like Nebraska, the Rockies and Texas."

" America's very rich," John said, " and it makes or grows absolutely everything."

" Nearly everyone seems to have a motor car," Alison suggested.

" You haven't really described America yet," said Daddy.

After a few seconds thought Alison pointed down to a great liner which looked like a toy on the blue sea. " That ship's going to New York from Europe," she said. " People will be on board going to start a new life in a new home—foreigners who will become Americans."

" Desmond told us that America was the 'Land of the Free'," said John. " That's it," replied Daddy, " The Land of the Free!"

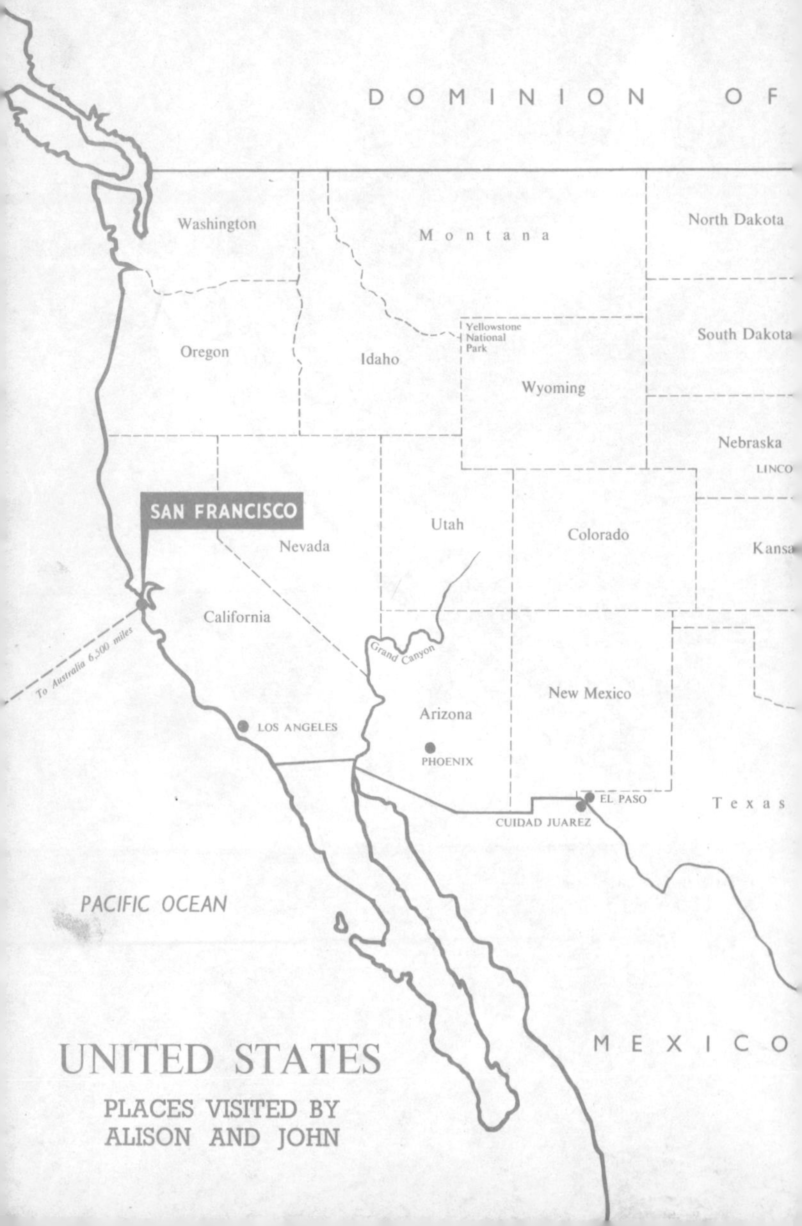

DOMINION OF

Washington

Montana

North Dakota

Oregon

Idaho

Yellowstone
National
Park

South Dakota

Wyoming

Nebraska

LINCO

SAN FRANCISCO

Nevada

Utah

Colorado

Kansa

California

Grand Canyon

To Australia 6,500 miles

Arizona

New Mexico

LOS ANGELES

PHOENIX

EL PASO

Texas

CUIDAD JUAREZ

PACIFIC OCEAN

UNITED STATES

PLACES VISITED BY
ALISON AND JOHN

MEXICO

CANADA

Lake Superior

Minnesota

Wisconsin

Lake Michigan

Lake Huron

M
i
c
h
i
g
a
n

Iowa

Illinois

CHICAGO

Indiana

Ohio

Lake Erie

Lake Ontario

New York

Maine

Ver.

N.H.

Mass.

Conn. R.I.

Missouri

Kentucky

FRANKFORT

West Virginia

Pennsylvania

PHILADELPHIA

N.J.

Virginia

M. BALTIMORE
D.
M.

WASHINGTON

To London 3,600 miles

NEW YORK

klahoma

Arkansas

Tennessee

North Carolina

Mississippi

Alabama

Georgia

South Carolina

HOUSTON

Louisiana

NEW ORLEANS

F
l
o
r
i
d
a

Ver.	Vermont
N.H.	New Hampshire
Mass.	Massachusetts
Conn.	Connecticut
R.I.	Rhode Island
N.J.	New Jersey
M.	Maryland
D.	Delaware

ATLANTIC OCEAN

ENGLAND & WALES
on the same scale

Series 587

Part of the speech made by Abraham Lincoln at Gettysburg
in 1863, during the American Civil War.

" *Four score and seven years ago our fathers brought forth on this
continent a new nation, conceived in liberty and dedicated to the
proposition that all men are created equal. Now we are engaged in
a great Civil War, testing whether this nation or any nation so
conceived can long endure. It is for us here to be dedicated to that
cause—that this nation, under God, shall have a new birth of
freedom—and that government of the people, by the people, for the
people, shall not perish from the earth.*"